The New Yorker Dogs

Front Cover: © 2001 Charles Barsotti, The New Yorker
Back Cover: © 2005 Michael Maslin, The New Yorker

Published by teNeues Verlag,
Am Selder 37, 47906 Kempen, Germany,
Tel.: (02152) 916-0, Fax: (02152) 916-111,
e-mail: verlag@teneues.de,
teNeues Publishing Company,
16 West 22nd Street, New York, NY 10010, USA,
Tel: (800) 352-0305, Fax: (212) 627-9511,
teNeues Publishing UK, London
and teNeues France, Paris
www.teneues.com
© The New Yorker Collection, cartoonbank.com
ISBN-10: 1-60160-006-2
ISBN-13: 978-1-60160-006-6
All rights reserved.

teNeues